MY BODY'S SUPERPOWER

JOURNAL

THE GIRLS' GUIDE TO GROWING UP HEALTHY DURING PUBERTY

MARYANN JACOBSEN

ISBN: 978-0-9995645-5-4

Cover Illustration by Hannah Patrico
Cover design and interior illustrations by Jeanine Henning, JH Illustrations
Book design by Maureen Cutajar, www.gopublished.com
Editing by Arnetta Jackson

First printing

Published by Jacobsen Publishing

JACOBSEN PUBLISHING

MaryannJacobsen.com

CONTENTS

INTRODUCTION

MY BODY'S SUPERPOWERS JOURNAL

I'm so glad you're here!

I created this journal to go along with *My Body's Superpower: The Girls' Guide to Growing a Healthy Body During Puberty.* Here you'll practice your body's 9 superpowers. Writing is a great way to track your progress, get feelings out, and work out problems.

Just like the book, this journal is separated into 9 sections for each superpower. There are quizzes to check your Super Knowledge, questions and exercises to help you get in touch with Body Talk, and lots of room to practice Time Travel and making Super Decisions. It's the Superpower Formula remember?

Use this journal to become familiar with using your superpowers and eventually you can move to another journal when you run out of room. You can fill out this journal in different ways. Maybe you read one chapter of the book and then come here to practice what you learned about. Or you read the entire book and start with the superpowers you need to practice most.

Either way, keep your journal in a private place where only you can find it and have a special place where you fill it out. Like all superheroes, it's important to take time to practice your superpowers. This journal helps you do that, one small step at a time.

SUPERPOWER 1

X-RAY VISION

X-RAY VISION

X-Ray Vision is learning about the changes going on in your body and accepting and using them to your advantage.

Let's start with a quiz to test your super knowledge. (Answers are at the back of the journal.)

QUIZ

1. Puberty is the second fastest growth spurt behind infancy. Is it longer or shorter than when you were a baby?

_____

2. What is most responsible for when you start and stop puberty?

    a)   nutrition
    b)   genes
    c)   sleep

3. There are 5 stages of puberty. In which stage does your period start?

_____

4. Do boys start puberty later or earlier than girls?

_____

5. Girls gain more body fat than boys in preparation for their menstrual cycle.

True or False (circle one)

QUESTIONS

What information in the Super Knowledge section surprised you the most?

_____

_____

_____

_____

What message is your body sending you about the stage of puberty you are in right now?

_____

_____

_____

_____

_____

_____

How do you feel about the way you are growing? Does it feel out of proportion?

_____

_____

_____

_____

Whether you are early (8-9), middle (10-12), or late to start puberty (13+), what are some ways you can accept and take advantage of where you are now?

_____

_____

_____

_____

No matter when it starts, there is an ending point to puberty. Can you ask someone you are close to how they felt after puberty? How do you think you'll feel when you're done growing?

_____

_____

_____

_____

_____

EXERCISES

When you get your period, track them below, writing the month in the space provided (or you can use an app if you have a smart phone). Remember, they may be irregular at first, but it's good to track them so you have a good idea when they're coming and you can get used to how your body feels.

MONTHLY TRACKER

P- period
C-cramps
L-light flow
H-heavy flow
M-moody

January

1 2 3 4 5 6 7 8 9 10 11 12 13 14 15 16 17 18 19 20 21 22 23 24 25 26 27 28 29 30 31

February

1 2 3 4 5 6 7 8 9 10 11 12 13 14 15 16 17 18 19 20 21 22 23 24 25 26 27 28 29
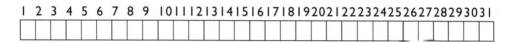

March

1 2 3 4 5 6 7 8 9 10 11 12 13 14 15 16 17 18 19 20 21 22 23 24 25 26 27 28 29 30 31
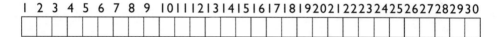

April

1 2 3 4 5 6 7 8 9 10 11 12 13 14 15 16 17 18 19 20 21 22 23 24 25 26 27 28 29 30

May

1 2 3 4 5 6 7 8 9 10 11 12 13 14 15 16 17 18 19 20 21 22 23 24 25 26 27 28 29 30 31

June

1 2 3 4 5 6 7 8 9 10 11 12 13 14 15 16 17 18 19 20 21 22 23 24 25 26 27 28 29 30

July

1 2 3 4 5 6 7 8 9 10 11 12 13 14 15 16 17 18 19 20 21 22 23 24 25 26 27 28 29 30 31

August

1 2 3 4 5 6 7 8 9 10 11 12 13 14 15 16 17 18 19 20 21 22 23 24 25 26 27 28 29 30 31

September

1 2 3 4 5 6 7 8 9 10 11 12 13 14 15 16 17 18 19 20 21 22 23 24 25 26 27 28 29 30

October

1 2 3 4 5 6 7 8 9 10 11 12 13 14 15 16 17 18 19 20 21 22 23 24 25 26 27 28 29 30 31

November

1 2 3 4 5 6 7 8 9 10 11 12 13 14 15 16 17 18 19 20 21 22 23 24 25 26 27 28 29 30

December

1 2 3 4 5 6 7 8 9 10 11 12 13 14 15 16 17 18 19 20 21 22 23 24 25 26 27 28 29 30 31

What PMS symptoms do you notice the week before your period? Take time to note what helps and what makes PMS symptoms worse.

_____

_____

_____

_____

_____

_____

_____

_____

_____

_____

_____

TIME TRAVEL AND SUPER DECISIONS

It's time for Time Travel! Use this section to consider how you'll feel in the future, when you and your friends are done growing and finished with puberty. What could happen if you try to change the course of puberty knowing that isn't in your power?

_____

_____

_____

_____

_____

_____

_____

_____

_____

_____

_____

_____

_____

_____

_____

Use the rest of the space to write about your decisions and how they worked out for you. You can learn from mistakes, celebrate successes, and make goals! Remember, Super Decisions utilize the Superpower formula of Super Knowledge, Body Talk, and Time Travel. Talking with others helps too.

_____

_____

_____

_____

_____

_____

_____

_____

_____

_____

_____

_____

_____

_____

_____

_____

_____

_____

_____

_____

_____

_____

_____

_____

SUPERPOWER 2

APPETITE SIGNALS

Appetite Signals are about trusting your body's signals for food and giving it what it needs to grow the way nature intended. If you need to review, check out Chapter 2 in the book.

QUIZ

1) What are the four appetite signals?

_____

_____

2) Genes highly influence the general size and shape of bodies referred to as a genetic blueprint.

True or False

3) What is the best way to ensure your body is growing the way nature intended? Circle the best answer.

a) Eat certain portions at specific times regardless of your body signals.

b) Plan regular meals and snacks and honor your hunger and fullness signals while eating.

c) Eat while you are doing other activities like watching TV or playing games.

4) Some foods are more filling than others. Which snack is most likely to be filling?

a) crackers

b) crackers and cheese

c) crackers, cheese, and grapes

5) Dieting makes appetite signals turn into alarms and puts the focus on food.

True or False

QUESTIONS

What information in the Super Knowledge section surprised you most?

_____

_____

Describe the different feelings you get from each appetite signal. Also note which one is the most challenging to listen to or easily turns into an alarm.

Hunger

_____

_____

Fullness

_____

_____

Satisfaction

_____

_____

Craving

_____

_____

Make notes here when you get most hungry and want to eat (other than at mealtime). Maybe you notice you are super hungry at lunch or you skip lunch on weekends, making you "hangry" (so hungry you feel angry!) in the afternoon.

_____

_____

_____

_____

If you have trouble recognizing your fullness or you can't seem to get full, what are some things you can try (check chapter two for some ideas) ?

_____

_____

_____

_____

Think about satisfaction and cravings. For example, if you aren't enjoying a meal it can be tough to get full from it. Or you may crave certain foods because you aren't satisfied at meals. What are some things you can do to increase satisfaction?

_____

_____

_____

_____

EXERCISES

Now let's take time to practice starting with hunger and fullness using the appetite scale. Use it with the different foods and meals you eat. Write down what you noticed about what affected your hunger and fullness signals. You can include information on satisfaction and cravings too.

Appetite Scale

1	**HANGRY!**	BAD MOOD, TIRED, NAUSEATED, WANT TO EAT ANYTHING
2	**HUNGRY:**	STOMACH GETTING EMPTY; FOOD SOUNDS GOOD
3	**HUNGER GONE:**	EATEN ENOUGH, BUT NOT FULLY SATISFIED/FULL
4	**FULL:**	SATISFIED AND COMFORTABLY FULL
5	**PAST FULL:**	UNCOMFORTABLY FULL STOMACH; MAY START ACHING/FEEL EXTENDED

Example:

Breakfast: *Rice Krispies with milk*

1	2	3	4	5

What did I notice?

It took away my hunger but was not really satisfying. I got hungry an hour before lunch at school and had trouble concentrating.

_____

_____

Breakfast_____

1	2	3	4	5

What did I notice?

_____

_____

Breakfast_____

1	2	3	4	5

What did I notice?

_____

_____

Snack_____

1	2	3	4	5

What did I notice?

_____

_____

Snack_____

1	2	3	4	5

What did I notice?

_____

_____

Snack_____

1	2	3	4	5

What did I notice?

_____

_____

Snack_____

1	2	3	4	5

What did I notice?

_____

_____

Lunch_____

I	2	3	4	5

What did I notice?

_____

_____

Lunch_____

I	2	3	4	5

What did I notice?

_____

_____

Lunch_____

I	2	3	4	5

What did I notice?

_____

_____

Dinner_____

1	2	3	4	5

What did I notice?

_____

_____

Dinner_____

1	2	3	4	5

What did I notice?

_____

_____

Dinner_____

1	2	3	4	5

What did I notice?

_____

_____

Dinner_____

1	2	3	4	5

What did I notice?

_____

_____

Dinner_____

1	2	3	4	5

What did I notice?

_____

_____

Try planning regular meals and snacks around your hunger. Experiment with times that work well (this may not be in your control because of family eating times).

Breakfast

_____

_____

_____

Snack

_____

_____

_____

Lunch

_____

_____

_____

Snack

_____

_____

_____

Dinner

_____

_____

_____

Energy-rich foods are important for food enjoyment, but too many can interfere with Super Functioning. So if you don't enjoy them, why eat them? Think about which are your absolute favorites by circling them, or filling others in below. Work with your parents to find sensible ways to include the ones you really love so you don't spend too much time thinking about them.

Cookies	Fries	_____
Cake	Chips	_____
Donuts	Pastries	_____
Ice cream	Candy bar	_____
Chocolate	Sweet drinks	_____
Sweet candy		_____

TIME TRAVEL AND SUPER DECISIONS

It's time for Time Travel! Use this section to consider how you'll feel in the future, when you are an expert at listening to and honoring your Appetite Signals. Also consider how you will feel if you don't.

_____

_____

_____

_____

_____

_____

_____

_____

_____

_____

_____

_____

Use the rest of the space to write about your decisions and how they worked out for you. You can learn from mistakes, set goals, and celebrate successes! Remember, Super Decisions utilize the Superpower formula of Super Knowledge, Body Talk, and Time Travel.

_____

_____

_____

_____

_____

SUPERPOWER 3

SUPER FUNCTIONING

Super Functioning is learning what your body needs during the adolescent growth spurt and applying nutrition into your eating so it's enjoyable and you feel great. Eating a variety of nutritious foods helps you do everything better!

QUIZ

Circle the correct answer.

1) The digestive system:
    a) helps break food down so the body can utilize nutrients
    b) needs fiber to help food move through
    c) hosts good bacteria to keep it healthy
    d) all of the above

2) Draw lines to the appropriate function for each body system.

nervous system	heart, arteries, and veins
skeletal system	brain, spinal cord, and nerves
circulatory system	your body's foundation
muscular system	skin, hair, nails, and sweat
integumentary system	allows your body to move

3) Vitamins and minerals provide the body with energy.

True or False

4) If your body isn't getting the nutrition it needs, you're most likely to hear from:

    a. digestive system
    b. skeletal system
    c. muscular system
    d. nervous system
    e. integumentary system
    f. a, d and e

5) What are the three macronutrients that provide the body with energy?

_____

_____

QUESTIONS

What information in the Super Knowledge section surprised you most?

_____

_____

_____

_____

How is your digestive system functioning? Do you have regular poop–every day or every other day? Are they soft and formed instead of hard or really loose? [see S in Super Practice and track symptoms in the Functioning Tracker.]

_____

_____

_____

_____

How is your energy level during the day? Do you find it hard to focus at certain times of the day? [See R in Super Practice, track symptoms in Functioning Tracker, and building a meal/snack.)

_____

_____

_____

_____

Does your skin look healthy and do your hair and nails feel strong? [see Super Practice and track symptoms in Functioning Tracker.]

_____

_____

_____

During puberty you need more water, and your body talks to you by signaling thirst. Do you have water with you during the day to answer the call of your body's signals? If not, what are some ideas to ensure you get enough water?

_____

_____

_____

_____

When we are satisfied with meals (meaning they taste good and we look forward to eating them), it's better for us. What are ways you can make taste a part of good nutrition for your body?

_____

_____

_____

_____

Here is your Functioning Tracker, a place to note when you feel good or notice super functioning. Even if you don't, mark it down and list some ideas for how to improve (see next two exercises). Remember, you are looking for patterns, so if something happens once, it may not mean anything.

FUNCTIONING TRACKER

Date	How do I feel?	What I ate/drank	Ideas to improve
6/5	Sluggish at soccer practice	Had a small lunch and snack of crackers and juice	Bigger lunch and balanced snack (add cheese) should give me more lasting energy

Date	How do I feel?	What I ate/drank	Ideas to improve

Date	How do I feel?	What I ate/drank	Ideas to improve

SUPER practice makes getting the nutrition you need simple. Write down some food ideas for incorporating all of the SUPER foods. If you don't like much in one category, write down ways to taste, experiment, and improve your pattern of eating. Check the book for ideas.

Stick with fruits and vegetables at most meals and snacks. They are crunchy and make a great addition to any meal or snack.

_____

_____

_____

_____

Up calcium-rich foods where you can. This includes dairy, non-dairy alternatives, and other foods that contain calcium. See calcium chart in the book.

_____

_____

_____

_____

Pick whole grains half the time. These are unrefined grains such as oats, whole wheat bread, brown rice, and quinoa.

_____

_____

_____

_____

_____

Eat fats too. Especially plant fat sources such as nuts and seeds, nut butters, avocados, and olive oil (these contain nutrients your body needs like vitamin E and magnesium).

_____

_____

_____

_____

Realize the power of protein. Round out meals with a protein source. Aim to include fish and beans a couple of times a week.

_____

_____

_____

_____

_____

_____

Practicing building balanced meals and snacks using the food groups. This gives you steady energy and the nutrition you need. Shoot for 2-3 food groups for a snack and 3-5 for a meal.

BUILD A MEAL OR SNACK

FOOD GROUP	FOOD TYPE
FRUITS	APPLES, PEARS, BANANAS, BLUE-BERRIES, RASPBERRIES, HONEYDEW, WATERMELON, GRAPEFRUIT, GRAPES, PRUNES, PLUMS, DRIED FRUIT
VEGETABLES	CARROTS, CAULIFLOWER, BRUSSELS SPROUTS, SWEET POTATO, CUCUMBER, ZUCCHINI, SQUASH, MUSHROOMS, TOMATOES, GREEN BEANS, SUGAR SNAP PEAS, CELERY

GRAINS	WHITE: WHITE BREAD, WHITE RICE, BAGELS, CRACKERS, PRETZELS, AND PASTA WHOLE GRAINS: OATS SUCH AS OATMEAL, POPCORN, CRACKERS, WHOLE CORN, WHOLE GRAIN PRETZELS, PASTA AND BREAD, BROWN RICE, QUINOA
DAIRY AND NONDAIRY SOURCES OF CALCIUM	MILK, CHEESE, YOGURT, COTTAGE CHEESE, NON-DAIRY ALTERNATIVES SUCH AS SOY, ALMOND, AND RICE MILK
PROTEIN FOODS	ANIMAL SOURCES: MEAT (BEEF, PORK, CHICKEN, ETC.), FISH, AND SHELLFISH PLANT SOURCES: BEANS, SOY, NUTS, AND SEEDS
FAT SOURCES	OILS, BUTTER, AVOCADO, NUTS, SEEDS, AND NUT BUTTERS

TIME TRAVEL AND SUPER DECISIONS

It's time for Time Travel! Use this section to consider how you'll feel in the future, when you are benefiting from Super Functioning (or not).

_____

_____

_____

_____

_____

_____

_____

_____

_____

_____

_____

_____

_____

_____

_____

Use the rest of the space to write about your decisions and how they worked out for you. Remember, Super Decisions utilize the Superpower formula of Super Knowledge, Body Talk, and Time Travel.

_____

_____

_____

_____

_____

_____

_____

_____

_____

_____

_____

_____

_____

_____

_____

_____

_____

_____

_____

_____

_____

_____

_____

_____

_____

_____

_____

SUPERPOWER 4

SUPER FOCUS

Super Focus is about identifying your mind's exercise and sleep helpers and then putting them to work to sharpen your mind and make life better.

QUIZ

1) Exercise helps which body systems? (Circle the best answer.)

a) circulatory system
b) skeletal system
c) muscular system
d) integumentary system
e) nervous system
f) all of them

2) Getting deep REM sleep is important for growth during puberty.

True or False

3) Put and E for exercise or an S for sleep to show how exercise and sleep help super focus and mood.

a) increases blood flow to the brain to help with learning
b) stores what you learned in your brain's long-term storage, clearing the mind for the next day's learning
c) releases endorphins to help you feel good
d) refreshes the mind and increases alertness during the day

4) Around the age of 12, your sleep cycle moves ahead by how many hours?

_____

5) Draw a line to the correct answer for how much sleep/exercise is recommended.

sleep 9-12 year olds   1 hour
sleep 13-18 year olds   8-10 hours
exercise for all   9-12 hours

QUESTIONS

What information from the Super Knowledge section surprised you most?

_____

_____

_____

_____

_____

How is your sleep going? Are you in sync with your internal clock? Do you feel well rested most of the time or feel tired throughout the day?

_____

_____

_____

_____

_____

Which activities help you relax and get ready for sleep?

_____

_____

_____

_____

Do you lead an active life? Has it slowed down or stayed the same as when you were younger?

_____

_____

_____

_____

_____

_____

_____

Do you consider myself an active person? If not, why?

_____

_____

_____

_____

What activities do you enjoy? [See list of examples in the book.]

_____

_____

_____

_____

Exercises

For a few weeks, track your focus and mood and your notes about your exercise and sleep. You should be able to start seeing how they both make you feel, about how much sleep makes you feel rested, and ways you can improve.

Focus Tracker

Date	How is my focus and mood?	Sleep notes	Activity notes	Ideas to improve
6/5	Distracted all day	Stayed up later than usual doing home-work	No change	Do homework right when I get home and go to bed early

Date	How is my focus and mood?	Sleep notes	Activity notes	Ideas to improve

Consider starting a sleep routine during the week. Experiment until you find something that works for you. Start with when it begins, which is about an hour before you typically get tired.

MY SLEEP ROUTINE

Start time	
Turn off devices (time)	
List of activities	
Ideal time to fall asleep	

Setting up a flexible activity routine and revising it helps you see where you can be active. For example, days you have gym class and sports practice means you were pretty active, but other days you may want to add activity breaks, and weekends are perfect for outings like hikes, bike riding, and walks or jogging.

MY ACTIVITY ROUTINE

	MON	TUES	WED	THURS	FRI	SAT	SUN
Activity breaks during the day to give me a boost							
Structured exercise (sports, dance, etc.)							
Gym class							

Activity outing							
Other:							

TIME TRAVEL

It's time for Time Travel! Use this section to consider how you'll feel in the future, when you are an expert at honing your Super Focus.

_____

_____

_____

_____

_____

_____

_____

_____

Use the rest of the space to write about your decisions around activity, sleep, and how they worked for you.

_____

_____

_____

_____

_____

_____

_____

_____

_____

_____

_____

_____

_____

_____

_____

_____

_____

_____

_____

_____

_____

_____

_____

_____

_____

_____

_____

_____

_____

_____

_____

_____

_____

_____

_____

_____

_____

_____

_____

SUPERPOWER 5

INTERNAL COMPASS

Internal Compass is discovering how your mind is developing and using your feelings and emotions to problem solve and live a better life. Be sure to ask a trusted adult for help with what you are feeling.

QUIZ

1) The reasoning center of the brain develops before the emotional center during adolescence.

True or False

2) Changes in moods during puberty are thought to be because girls:

a) are being exposed to the hormone estrogen for the first time
b) are more self conscious, feeling like everyone is watching them
c) are more sensitive to stress
d) all of the above can affect mood

3) An activity that takes up extra energy in the brain is called a:

4) All your feelings (no matter how uncomfortable) are your body's way of sending you important information.

True or false

5) Circle all of the activities that are good exercise for your mind:

practicing gratitude
mindfulness
overthinking everything
being kind to yourself
binge-watching TV
participating in energy-producing activities
making decisions quickly
pausing and calming down before making a decision

QUESTIONS

What information in the Super Knowledge section surprised you most?

_____

.

_____

_____

_____

_____

_____

What feelings and corresponding emotions are most challenging for you?

_____

_____

_____

_____

_____

_____

Do you notice any situations that tend to overwhelm you adding stress to your life?

_____

_____

_____

_____

_____

What are some energy-giving activities that help to calm you in the face of stressful or difficult situations? Circle or add your own.

jumping
deep breathing
talking with someone
taking a walk
bike riding
reading
listening to music
playing music
other

_____

_____

_____

_____

_____

EXERCISES

Track your feelings/physical sensations, what emotion you are experiencing, and what it might be trying to tell you. Often emotions are telling us we need to feel something, change or notice something, or that our thoughts need some reframing (see Thought Holes in next section for explanation and examples).

Here's a list of emotions: anxiety, worry, disappointment, anger, guilt, loneliness, envy, embarrassment, sadness, feeling overwhelmed, surprise, joy, disgust, hopeful, bored, eager, excited, proud, relieved, self conscious, irritated, uncertain, determined, peaceful.

EMOTION TRACKER

Feeling/Physical Sensation	Emotion	What could it be trying to tell you?

As discussed in *My Body's Superpower*, thoughts are not facts. Think of these thoughts as guesses that the mind can get wrong. So the times your feelings and emotions are due to your own thoughts, check to see if those thoughts have holes. Below are some examples and space to write.

THOUGHT HOLES

Common Thought Holes	Challenge	Alternative
Jumping to conclusions "My friend must be mad at me because she didn't wave."	How can I know what someone else is thinking -- it's their mind!	"I don't know what's going on; my friend may have just had a bad morning."
Black and white "Nothing ever works out for me."	Really? Sometimes things are going well and other times I'm more challenged. It's not black or white.	"Instead of judging, I will try to learn and improve when things don't go my way."
Perfectionist thinking "If I don't get a goal in the game, I'm a bad soccer player and no one will like me."	Why should I hold myself to this unrealistic standard? An off performance doesn't make me a bad soccer player.	"I will strive to be better at soccer, but will expect mistakes and setbacks as part of the process."
Comparisonitis "Everyone does better at math than I do."	How can I know how everyone does in math? They are probably thinking the same thing about me!	"I will work to be successful in my own way."

Common Thought Holes	Challenge	Alternative

Try to take five minutes each day to review SHARP and practice it (review below). At the end of the day you can practice mindfulness and being grateful (SH), while reviewing self-care, activities, and decision making suggestions (ARP) See the first example in the SHARP Tracker. below. When you run out of room you can do more later in the Decision area or in a separate journal.

BE SHARP

Start with mindfulness -- sit in silence for five minutes a day.

Have a grateful attitude -- write down one thing you are grateful for.

Always be kind to yourself - catch yourself when you're being critical, and give yourself some kindness and understanding.

Re-direct to energy-giving activities -- feeling stressed; note activities that calm you.

Pause and calm down before making decisions -- when upset, wait to make a decision and try deep breathing.

SHARP TRACKER

S 6/17 *(5 min)*
_____

H 6/17 *grateful for my math teacher*
_____

A 6/17 *got a B on my English test but worked really hard*
_____

R 6/17 *feeling stressed about school, a bike ride helped*
_____

P 6/17 *unsure which elective to choose, but have two more days; will work on calming down*
_____

S

_____

H

_____

A

_____

R

_____

P

_____

S

_____

H

_____

A

_____

R

_____

P

_____

S

_____

H

_____

A

_____

R

_____

P

_____

S

_____

H

_____

A

_____

R

_____

P

_____

S

_____

H

_____

A

_____

R

_____

P

_____

S

_____

H

_____

A

_____

R

_____

P

_____

TIME TRAVEL AND SUPER DECISIONS

It's time for Time Travel! Use this section to consider how you'll feel in the future, when you become more familiar with your inner world and are able to use your Internal Compass. What do you think might happen if you aren't in touch with what's going on inside you?

_____

_____

_____

_____

_____

_____

_____

_____

_____

Use the rest of the space to write about your decisions around feelings and emotions. You can also continue your SHARP practice.

_____

_____

_____

_____

_____

_____

_____

_____

_____

_____

_____

_____

_____

_____

_____

_____

_____

_____

_____

_____

_____

_____

_____

_____

SUPERPOWER 6

SUPER FRIENDS

Super Friends is acknowledging the importance of connection and being thoughtful when forming and maintaining friendships.

QUIZ

1. Positive and meaningful relationships are good for your health.

True or False

2. Name three qualities that make a good friend:

_____

3. Connect the types of bullying on the left, with the right answer on the right.

relational   Using physical gestures to
                                  terrorize someone

cyber   Using worlds to put someone
                                  down

physical   Bullying over the internet

verbal   Excluding others from a group

4. What are helpful ways to compare yourself to others?

a)   If you find you consistently perform better than others at some-
     thing, it helps you figure out what your unique talents are and/or
     what you enjoy doing.
b)   If it's envy you feel, try to figure out what it might be trying to
     tell you.
c)   Realize some envy is normal and not to be taken so seriously.
d)   All of the above.

5. Empathy is putting yourself in someone else's shoes and considering
how they feel.

True or False

QUESTIONS

What information in the Super Knowledge section surprised you the
most?

_____

_____

_____

In what ways are you a Super Friend to your friends? Are there ways
you can improve?

_____

_____

_____

_____

_____

Although it's normal to want to fit in, it's more important to feel like you belong. In what ways do you feel like you belong with your friends?

_____

_____

_____

_____

_____

What type of social comparisons do you tend to make and what could they be trying to tell you?

_____

_____

_____

_____

_____

Do you feel like you belong to any communities? If not, what are some ways you can improve on this?

_____

_____

_____

_____

_____

EXERCISES

When you get certain feelings around friends, take time to identify the emotion and write down the potential "watch out" or "good sign." This includes social comparisons about any same-age peer. Review Chapter 6 in the book for more information.

FRIEND FEELINGS

Emotion	Watch Out	Good Sign	Comparison	Not Helpful	Helpful
Invisible around friend	*X*		*She's outgoing and pretty*	*Trying to be like her will mean I'm less of me*	*Maybe I need to work on my unique qualities and let them shine*

Emotion	Watch Out	Good Sign	Comparison	Not Helpful	Helpful

Nowadays, young people spend time connecting on phones by texting or social media but this does not replace face-to-face interactions. Talk to your parents and consider planning time to see friends more often. If you're involved in a theater community at school, for instance, maybe you can plan to see musicals around town. Or you can have a movie night asking a parent to chaperone.

Month:						
SUN	**MON**	**TUE**	**WED**	**THURS**	**FRI**	**SAT**

Month:						
SUN	**MON**	**TUE**	**WED**	**THURS**	**FRI**	**SAT**

Month:						
SUN	**MON**	**TUE**	**WED**	**THURS**	**FRI**	**SAT**

TIME TRAVEL AND SUPER DECISIONS

It's time for Time Travel! Use this section to consider how you'll feel in the future, when you take time to build and maintain friendships and communities—or if you don't; or if you just settle for friends that aren't Super Friends.

_____

_____

_____

_____

_____

_____

_____

_____

_____

_____

Use the rest of the space to write about your decisions around friends and social experiences. You can learn from mistakes and celebrate successes! Remember, Super Decisions utilize the Superpower formula of Super Knowledge, Body Talk, and Time Travel. So when you need to, review the book!

_____

_____

_____

_____

_____

_____

_____

_____

_____

_____

SUPERPOWER 7

SUPER YOU!

Super You is about taking time to get to know yourself, the type of person you want to be, and learning to listen to that wise voice directing you to your future (super) self. In a world full of people, there's still only one Super You!

QUIZ

1. As long as I do well in school, it shouldn't matter if I learn other life skills like cooking and cleaning up.

True or False

2. Someone of strong character would:

a) do the right thing when no one is watching and there is no reward
b) learn from their mistakes
c) do things out of fear of what others will think
d) a and b

3. Circle the example that shows a person has a growth mindset after getting a poor grade on a math test:

a) Blaming the teacher for not covering the material or making the test too hard
b) Thinking she just doesn't get the material and is doomed to always do poorly in math
c) Reviews her mistakes and works to improve for next time

4. Outside goals are based on what others value and are more focused on outcomes. Inside goals come from what you value, and you're more focused on enjoying the process. Write an "I" next to the examples of inside goals, and an "O" for those that are outside goals.

a) Getting straight A's
b) Learning, and personal growth
c) Being popular
d) Creating meaningful relationships
e) Building good health to feel good
f) Doing what it takes to look good so others will notice

5. Your wise inner voice helps direct you to your _____self.

QUESTIONS

What surprised you most about the Super Knowledge section of this Chapter?

_____

_____

_____

_____

What are some natural rewards you get from showing strong character (hint: they result in good feelings).

_____

_____

_____

_____

When you feel stressed, it may have to do with outside goals and worrying what others think. What times do you feel stress and how can switching to inside goals help?

_____

_____

_____

_____

In what areas of your life do you feel independent, and what are others that you don't? What messages does your body send you about this?

_____

_____

_____

_____

Describe a time your wise inner voice has surprised you, nudging you to do something different than what you've done before. Now ask a parent or trusted adult when this happened to them.

_____

_____

_____

_____

EXERCISES

When you're feeling stressed about something you need to do, see if it's an outside goal getting in the way. Once you identify the outside goal and stress, redirect to an inside goal and see how you feel.

OUTSIDE/INSIDE GOAL TRACKER

Identify the Outside Goal	Feeling/Emotion	Redirect to an Inside Goal	Feeling
I need an A in math to take advanced classes and get into college	Tightness in chest/ anxiety	I enjoy math and the challenges of problem solving. I will work on it and accept the outcome.	Body feels calm/peaceful

Identify the Outside Goal	Feeling/Emotion	Redirect to an Inside Goal	Feeling

Life skills are important. Here's a good list but feel free to add to it and ask your parents for input. Make a simple, achievable goal, and write down the first small step. Once you've reach this goal, move on to the next one.

LIFE SKILLS GOAL SMALL STEP

Life skills	Goal	Small step
Make simple meals/snacks		
Clean room		
Do laundry		
Take out trash		
Take out recycle		
Sweep		
Do the dishes		
Clean the bathroom		
Be able to type		
Manage money		
Take a babysitting course		
Time management/write in calendar and to-dos		

Learn CPR		
Mend/sew buttons		
Wash the car		

List hobbies and areas that get your juices flowing and/or that you feel you have special talents. This can be a hobby you learn on your own or something that you decide needs more structured learning (like in school or an after-school activity).

Area of interest	How can I do it more?

TIME TRAVEL

It's time for Time Travel! Use this section to consider how you'll feel in the future, when you are more of *you* and feel proud of who you've become and what you do. How will you feel if you just live your life to please others to get their stamp of approval?

_____

_____

_____

_____

_____

_____

_____

_____

_____

_____

Use the rest of the space to write about your Super Decisions. Write it all down -- mistakes and successes. Remember, Super Decisions utilize the Superpower formula of Super Knowledge, Body Talk, and Time Travel. So when you need to, review the book!

_____

_____

_____

_____

_____

_____

_____

_____

_____

_____

_____

_____

_____

_____

_____

_____

_____

_____

_____

_____

_____

_____

_____

_____

_____

_____

_____

_____

_____

_____

_____

_____

_____

_____

_____

_____

_____

_____

_____

_____

_____

_____

_____

_____

_____

_____

_____

_____

_____

_____

_____

_____

_____

SUPERPOWER 8

CRITICAL THINKING

Critical Thinking is demanding and seeking evidence for what is presented as true. Without evidence, it's just another opinion.

QUIZ

1. Cultural faves are not right or wrong, they are just preferences of a culture.
True or False

2. Draw a line for what best describes the real world and virtual world.
real world   man made to look a certain way
virtual world   has variety and is complex
                                              unrealistic photos, images and
                                                 videos
                                              everyday looking people
                                              some products helpful, others not
                                                 so much
                                              products look amazing
                                              everyone seems so perfect and
                                                 happy
                                              everyone has a mix of happy,
                                                 neutral, and challenging times

3. Circle the ways media images are unrealistic.

a) They are Photoshopped to manipulate size and remove blemishes
b) professional hair, makeup, and styling is done
c) filters are added
d) all of the above

4. When it comes to online articles and blogs, would the following be a *red flag* or a *good sign?* (circle one in the question)

Makes strong claims without citing research, gives extremes advice, and says all the experts have it wrong

5. Someone that critically thinks does this one, important thing:

_____

QUESTIONS

What information in the Super Knowledge section surprised you most?

_____

_____

_____

_____

_____

Being a digital native (someone who was born into a technology-based society) affects how you interact in the real world. What do you think are some pros and cons to being a digital native?

_____

_____

_____

_____

_____

_____

Have you ever felt negative about your body or life after viewing media images and social media sites? If so, what questions can you ask to change that to a more neutral or positive feeling?

_____

_____

_____

_____

_____

_____

Have you ever thought a product was super cool only to bring it home and be disappointed? Explain.

_____

_____

_____

_____

_____

What looks-oriented stereotypes do you notice in the movies and shows you watch?

_____

_____

_____

_____

_____

EXERCISES

When you are visiting the virtual world and it affects how you feel in a negative way, jot down how you're feeling here. Then ask questions and see how it changes how you feel and interact with the virtual world.

CRITICAL THINKING TRACKER

Type of media	Questions to ask	How I feel before	How I feel after
Images	Is this what everyday people look like? How has this image been touched up?		
Advertising	Is this product as good as it looks on TV? Does it sound too good to be true? Is this advertising instilling a belief that isn't in line with my values?		
Social Media	Does this picture show how this person's life really is? Am I spending too much time on social media instead of with in-person interactions?		

TV Shows	Does this show demonstrate how people really are? Who created it and what was their intention? What stereotype are they presenting here?		
News articles and Blogs	What signs show me this information is accurate or not?		

Embracing who you are can be very powerful. Take some time to consider what the virtual world might view as an imperfection, but which you are learning is powerful in your life. Remember what Reema Zeeman said about realizing how her troublesome imperfections were part of her complexity and authentic power.

Virtual Imperfection	Makes Me Powerful
The virtual word prefers slender bodies and doesn't value bigger and muscular bodies on girls like me.	I am strong in the sports I play which include softball and volleyball. My strong body helps me compete and empowers me.

TIME TRAVEL

It's time for Time Travel! Use this section to consider how you'll feel in the future, when you critically think about the virtual world. What if you don't, and just believe all it tells you?

_____

_____

_____

_____

_____

_____

_____

_____

_____

_____

_____

Use the rest of the space to write about your Super Decisions. Write it all down -- mistakes and successes. Remember, Super Decisions utilize the Superpower formula of Super Knowledge, Body Talk, and Time Travel. So when you need to, review the book!

_____

_____

_____

_____

_____

_____

_____

_____

_____

_____

_____

_____

_____

SUPERPOWER 9

THE PRESSURE REDUCER

The Pressure Reducer is being able to identify pressure and reduce it by using your values, appreciation mindset, and by focusing on what works for you.

QUIZ

1. What is on the receiving end of pressure, acting like a tug-of-war game?

_____

2. The pressure about bodies typically can come from:

a) How others talk about their body
b) How others talk about others' bodies (and possibly yours)
c) How you internalize these pressures and do it to yourself
d) All of the above

3. Draw a line from the phrase on the right, connecting it with the correct answer on the left:

Opinion	promising area with new science
Emerging	it worked for someone, so they talk about it
Fact	we know it's true, based on research

4. Put a big "A" next to the statements that indicate a disapproving mindset and a little "a" to the ones that indicate an appreciation mindset:

Focusing on body flaws and how you want to change them
Noticing and appreciating your body's good qualities and uniqueness

Wearing clothes to cover up your body

Wearing clothes that make your body feel good

Feeling uncomfortable in your body because you wish it looked different

Feeling comfortable in your body because you accept it and give it what it needs

5. Focusing on our values or doing a value check, is a good first step when we're feeling pressure.

True or False

QUESTIONS

What information in the Super Knowledge section surprised you most?

_____

_____

_____

_____

_____

In what areas of your life do you feel the most pressure? How does your body feel, physically, when you feel pressure?

_____

_____

_____

_____

_____

Do you feel pressure about your body or notice that others feel pressure about theirs?

_____

_____

_____

_____

Are there any areas you put a lot of pressure on yourself for, even when others don't? What assumptions are you making, and are they true? (Example: mistakes mean failure.)

_____

_____

_____

_____

_____

Write down five of your top values:

_____

_____

_____

_____

_____

EXERCISES

When you feel pressure, write in the following chart. Use your values, appreciation mindset, or what works for you to turn things around. You may use one or all three, depending on the situation.

Identify pressure and how you feel	1. Value check	2. Apprecia-tion mindset	3. What works for you	How do you feel?
I need to be in a good mood all the time or people won't like me.	*I value listening to my feelings even when they are uncomfortable.*	*I'm glad my body sends me messages.*	*Holding in feelings may work for some people, but not me!*	*Relieved – I can be myself, and be in a bad mood sometimes.*

Identify pressure and how you feel	1. Value check	2. Apprecia-tion mindset	3. What works for you	How do you feel?

Much of the pressure girls feel can be from being hard on themselves. Use the following chart to note when you are hard on yourself and turn things around to be more self-compassionate. How does that help your motivation?

SELF-COMPASSION TRACKER

Hard on yourself	Why?	Motivation	Kinder to yourself	Why?	Motivation
I can't believe I messed up at band practice!	I need to be the best at band or else I'll never make it.	Low—I don't feel like practicing.	Everyone messes up. I'm part of the worldwide "mess-up" club.	When learning new pieces, mistakes are part of the learning process.	High—I love the feeling of mastering music, so will practice more.

Hard on yourself	Why?	Motivation	Kinder to yourself	Why?	Motivation

TIME TRAVEL

It's time for Time Travel! Use this section to consider how you'll feel in the future, when you master your pressure-reducer abilities.

_____

_____

_____

_____

_____

_____

_____

_____

_____

_____

_____

_____

Use the rest of the space to write about your Super Decisions. Write it all down -- mistakes and successes. Remember, Super Decisions utilize the Superpower formula of Super Knowledge, Body Talk, and Time Travel. So when you need to, review the book!

_____

_____

_____

_____

_____

_____

_____

_____

_____

_____

_____

_____

QUIZ ANSWERS

SUPERPOWER 1: X-RAY VISION

1. Longer. Babies have a 2-year growth spurt and for girls the average is 4 years
2. b
3. Step 4
4. Boys start puberty later by about 2 years
5. True

SUPERPOWER 2: APPETITE SIGNALS

1. Hunger, fullness, satisfaction, and craving
2. True
3. b
4. c
5. True

SUPERPOWER 3: SUPER FUNCTIONING

1. d
2. nervous system — brain, spinal cord, and nerves
   skeletal system— your body's foundation
   circulatory system — heart, arteries, and veins
   muscular system — allows your body to move
   integumentary system — skin, hair, nails, and sweat

3. False
4. f
5. Carbohydrates, protein, and fat

SUPERPOWER 4: SUPER FOCUS

1. f
2. True
3. E, S, E, S
4. 2 hours
5. 9-12 sleep --9-12; 13-18 -- 8-10
   exercise -- 1 hour

SUPERPOWER 5: INTERNAL COMPASS

1. False
2. d
3. Stressor
4. True
5. practicing gratitude, mindfulness, being kind to yourself, participating in energy-giving activities, pausing and calming down
   before making a decision

SUPERPOWER 6: SUPER FRIENDS

1. True
2. Pick three of (or maybe something else not on this list): Can be
   yourself, treats you well,
   doesn't pressure you to do something after you said no, wel-
   comes your other friends,
   can be trusted, is reliable most of the time, treats the people
   around her respectfully, happy

for you when you succeed, is honest with themselves and you, and is a good listener
3. relational -- excluding others from a group
cyber -- bullying over the internet
physical -- using physical gestures to terrorize someone
verbal -- using words to put someone down
4. d
5. True

SUPERPOWER 7: SUPER YOU

1. False
2. d) a and b
3. Reviews her mistakes and where she went wrong and works to improve for next time
4. O, I, O, I, I, O
5. future

SUPERPOWER 8: CRITICAL THINKING

1. True
2. Virtual world — manmade to look a certain way, unrealistic photos, images, and videos, products look amazing, everyone seems so perfect and happy
Real world— has variety and is complex, everyday looking people, some products are helpful, others not so much, everyone has a mix of happy, neutral, and challenging times
3. d
4. red flag
5. Asks questions

SUPERPOWER 9: PRESSURE REDUCER

1. resistance
2. d
3. opinion — it worked for someone so they talk about it
   emerging — promising area with new science
   fact — we know it's true, based on the research
4. A, a, A, a, A, a
5. True

Made in the USA
Middletown, DE
26 June 2022

67830440R00078